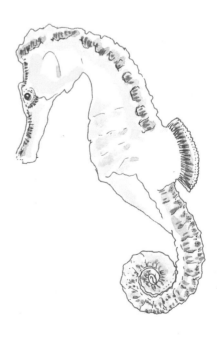

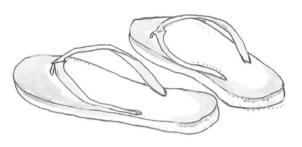

There's A Story On My Mama

Written by Jane Oehm

Illustrated by Katie Rennuit

Copyright © Ledflo Publishing, 2023 London, UK
All rights reserved

ISBN 978-I-8383290-I-3 (Paperback)

Thank you to the phenomenal women who inspired this story
and to all mums, however you come, for doing what you do.
You not only deserve to be seen but celebrated and lionised too.

There's a story on my mama there's a seahorse on her hip,
she had it tattooed there on her favourite diving trip.

Deep in the blue ocean on the search for a whale,
she saw a seahorse giving birth... it must have been a male.

There's a story on my mama she has dark spots from the sun, and knows that's where they're from as they weren't there when she was young.

She would bask on the beach with her besties for hours,
then head for a drink on their balcony of flowers.

There's a story on my mama there's a nick upon her knee,
she fell off her scooter in Koh Samui.

The nurse patched her up, he was HERO of the day!
It didn't stop Mum dancing the hot nights away.

There's a story on my mama a hole sits above her lip,
it used to have a stud in it but HR had a flip.

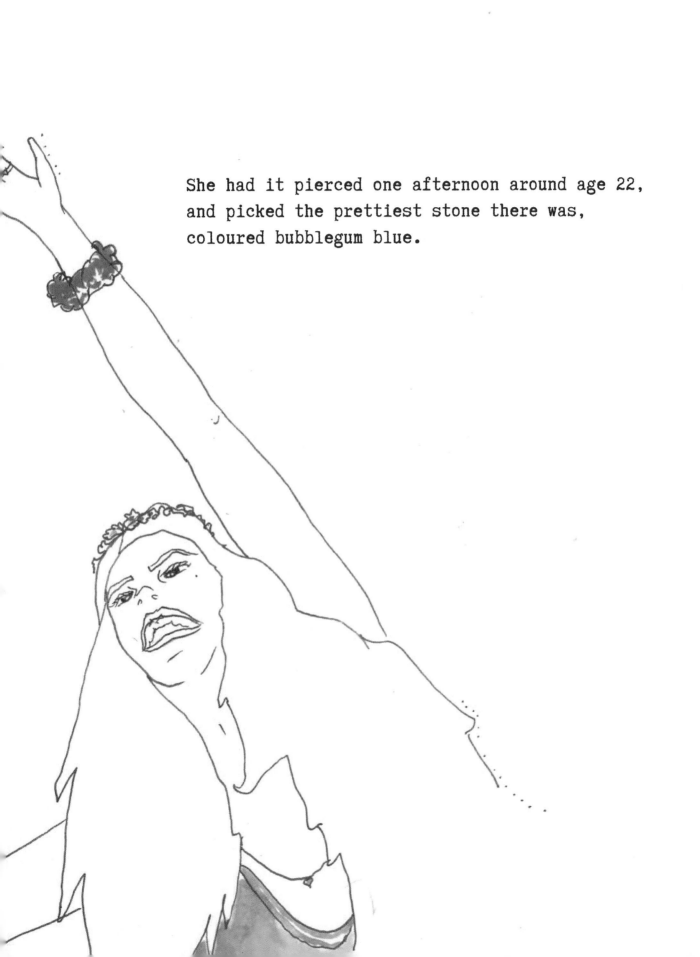

She had it pierced one afternoon around age 22,
and picked the prettiest stone there was,
coloured bubblegum blue.

There's a story on my mama she has a beautiful bald head,
it's called alopecia and it caused her hair to shed.

She once had curls a lot like mine and flung them 'round at gigs,
now she ROCKS the stage with big earrings
or sometimes wears a wig.

There's a story on my mama squiggles run across her thighs,
"Stretch marks are what they're called my love,
they can appear no matter your size."

She grew SUPER tall one summer, her skin just couldn't keep up.
That extra height helped her team bring home the mighty cup.

There's a story on my mama her cheeks flush when she feels sad,
"Big people have big feelings too," she sighs, smiling at Dad.

"Sometimes we can pinpoint why, sometimes it's a muddle.
Please know I'm here for you when you feel the struggle."

There's a story on my mama she has one foot missing,
it happened on a childhood trip while out ice fishing.

When reeling in her rainbow trout she went WHOOPSIES,
which saw her go from ten to five cute little tootsies.

There's a story on my mama there's a scar upon her tummy,
she says it's from me hiding on the night she became my mummy.

I didn't want to exit but eviction time had come,
so they gave her a C-section after making her waist numb.

There are stories on my mama and over time they'll appear on me,
that is one sure thing life can guarantee.

Everyone has lumps and bumps, scars or a tattoo,
some people have one body part where others have two.

Celebrating differences is what it's all about,
and your mama is her own person who LOVES you beyond doubt.

Look closely at the ones you love,
you'll see stories on them too...

A sneak peek into something which they've gone through.

Thank you to the community of women who helped bring this together.

From proofreads, editing and ideas,

to your time, stories and skillsets being offered so generously.

May we continue to lift one another.

Printed in Poland
by Amazon Fulfillment
Poland Sp. z o.o., Wrocław

21248514R00018